THEMES AND MUSIC FOR SOLO PIANO MADE POPULAR BY TV ADS

CLASSIC ADS

Exclusive distributors:
Chester Music
(a division of Music Sales Limited)
8/9 Frith Street,
London W1D 3JB,
England.

Order No. CH65989
ISBN 0-7119-9746-2

Music processed by Note-orious.
Music arranged by Simon Lesley (except Sarabande,
Adagio For Strings, Air On A G String, Sleepers Awake,
In The Hall Of The Mountain King, Nessun Dorma,
Chasing Sheep Is Best Left To Shepherds and
Theme from Jean de Florette).

Printed in the United Kingdom .

THEMES AND MUSIC **FOR SOLO PIANO** MADE POPULAR BY TV ADS

CLASSIC ADS

CHESTER MUSIC
London / New York / Paris / Sydney / Copenhagen / Berlin / Madrid / Tokyo

LEVI'S JEANS

SARABANDE

from 'Harpsichord Suite in D minor'

By George Frideric Handel

a tempo
18
cresc.
22
f
dim.
p
26
molto rit.
30

THE TIMES

ADAGIO FOR STRINGS

By Samuel Barber

r.h.
Ped.
Ped.
p
l.h.
Ped.

Ped.
mf
mf
cresc.

f
Ped.
Ped.
Ped.
cresc. sempre
ff
Ped.
Ped.
pp
p

p
morendo
pp
Ped.

MAGNUM/KRONENBOURG 1664

SLIP INTO SOMETHING MORE COMFORTABLE

By Mark Blackburn, Julius Waters, Fred Karger & Robert Wells

17
sub. pp
(mp)
21
sfz
25
mf
(mp)
29

33
37
8vb

SMIRNOFF

1492: CONQUEST OF PARADISE

By Vangelis

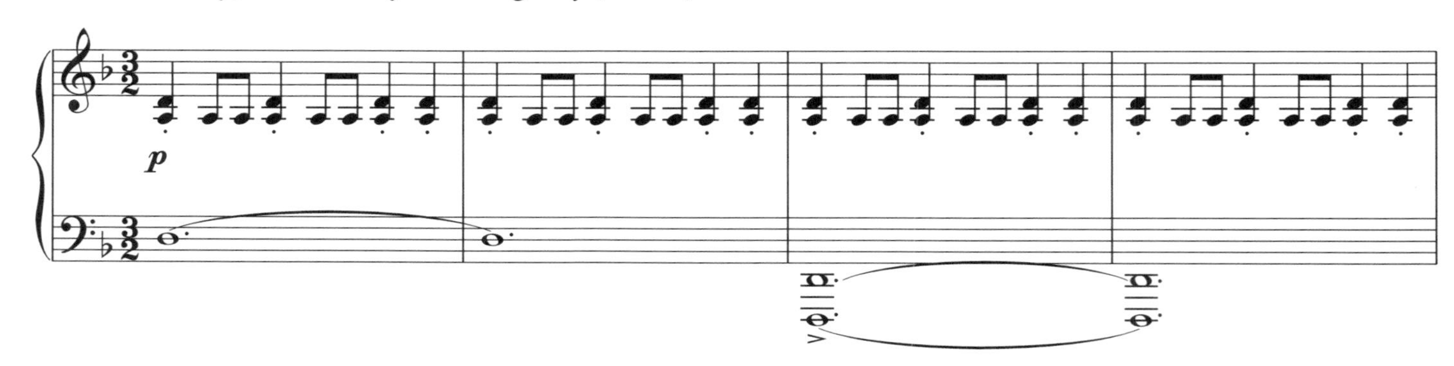

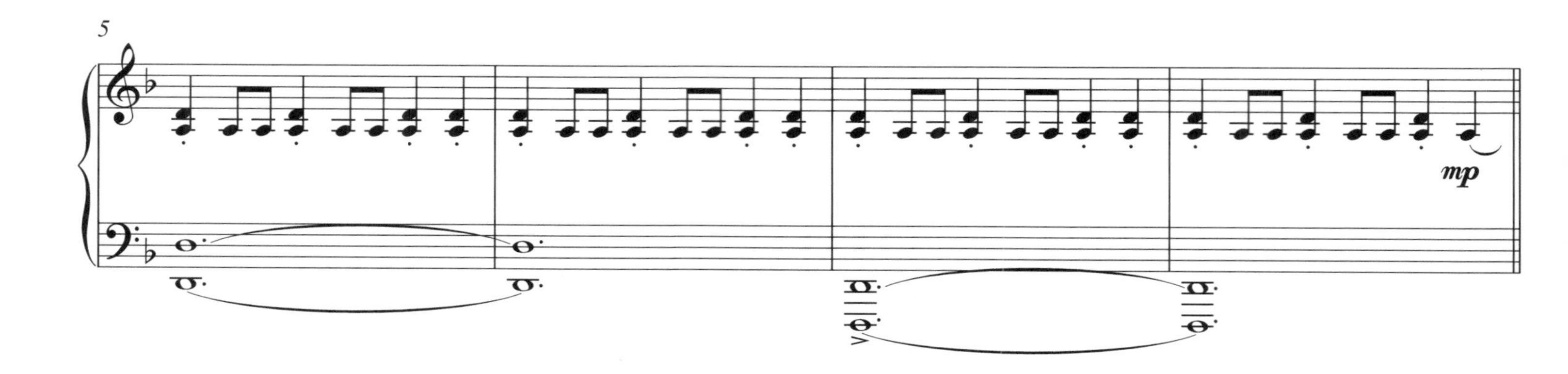

15
18
cresc. poco a poco
21
25
mf
29

47
50
1.
2.
mp
mp
dim. poco a poco
53
56
59

62
65
dim.
68
71
8va
loco
Ped.
74
pp
dim.

HARRODS

LASCIA CH'IO PIANGA

from 'Rinaldo'

By George Frideric Handel

25
30
p
35
tr
40
pp
45

50
55
60
65
f
69

BRITISH AIRWAYS

FLOWER DUET

from 'Lakmé'

By Leo Delibes

poco rit.
17

a tempo
rit. al fine
21

24
molto ten.

HAMLET

AIR ON A G STRING

from 'Orchestral Suite No.3'

By Johann Sebastian Bach

Molto rall.
Ped.

LLOYDS BANK

SLEEPERS AWAKE

from 'Cantata No.140'

By Johann Sebastian Bach

Allegretto tranquillo

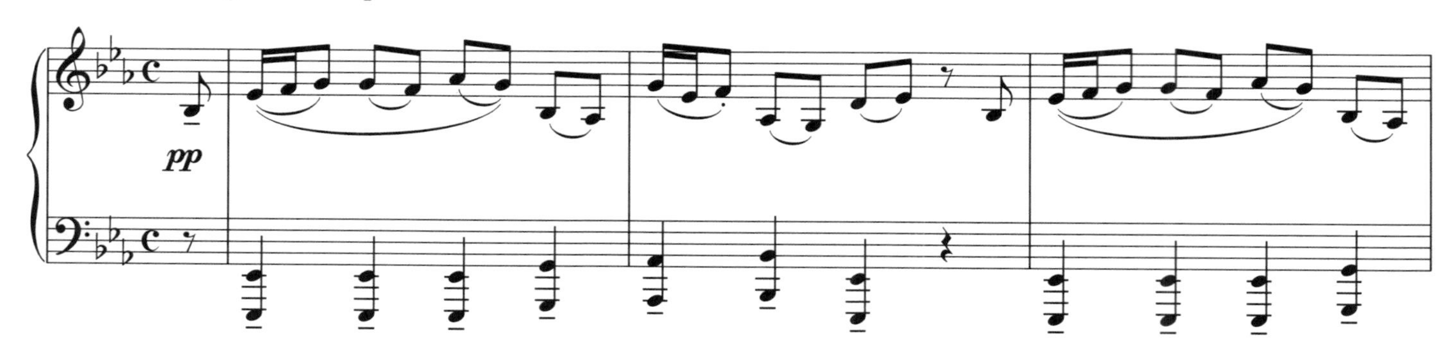

13
mf
r.h.
16
r.h.
19
ten.
22
25
tr

28
tr
3
r.h.
31
r.h.
34
37
poco cresc.
40
tr
dim.
poco più f

43
più p
46
espressivo molto
49
dolce
tr
51
semplice
tr

DRAMBUIE/ALTON TOWERS

IN THE HALL OF THE MOUNTAIN KING

from 'Peer Gynt Suite No.1'

By Edvard Grieg

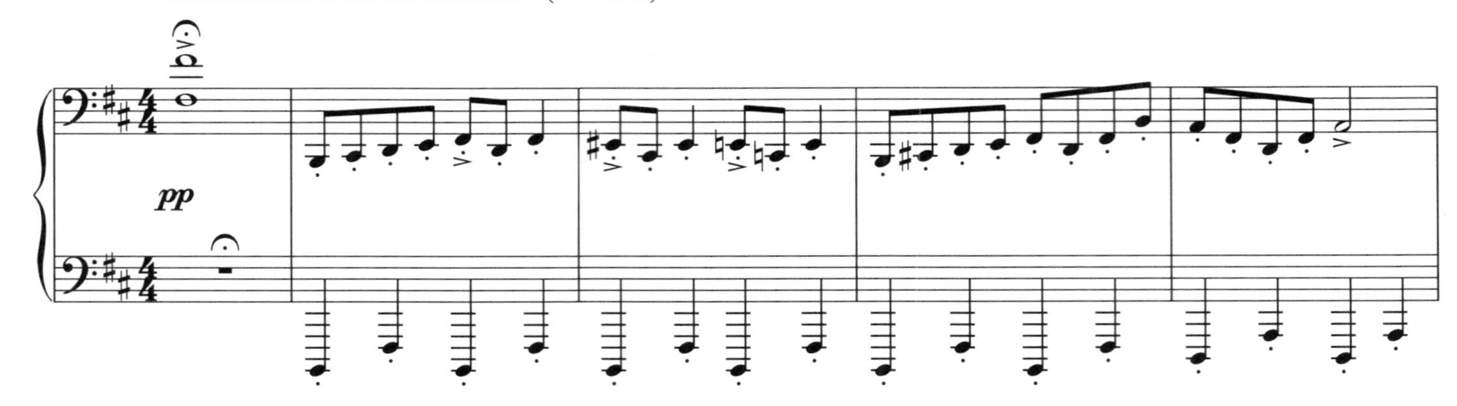

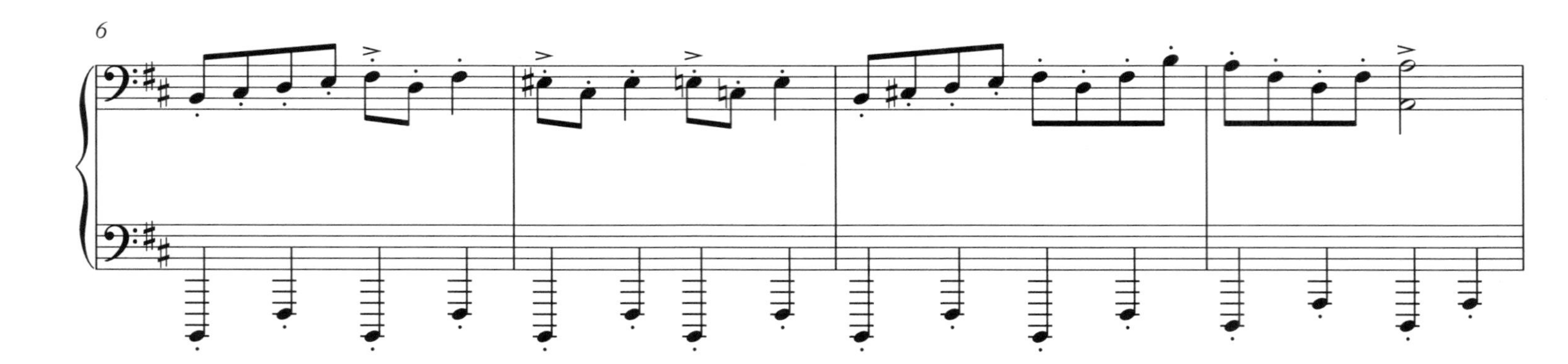

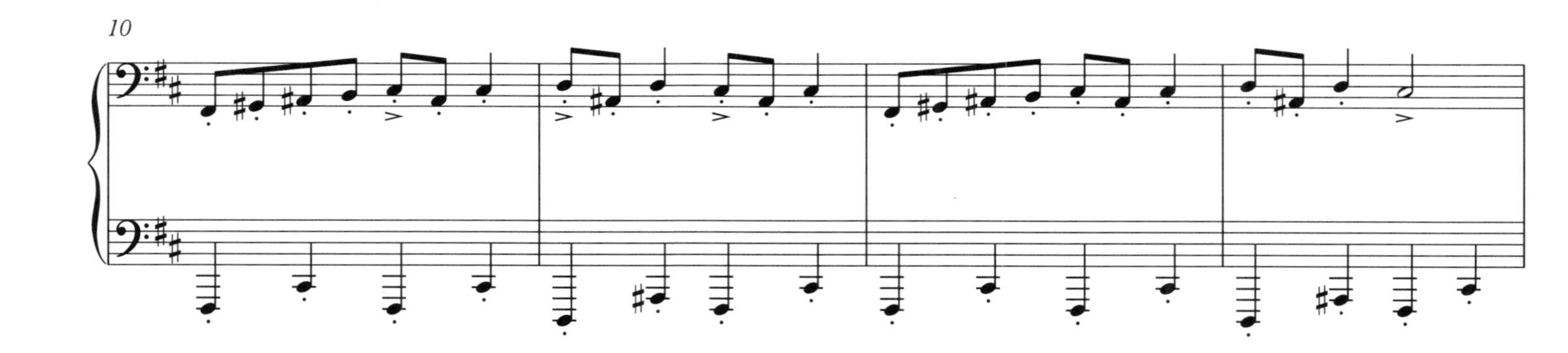

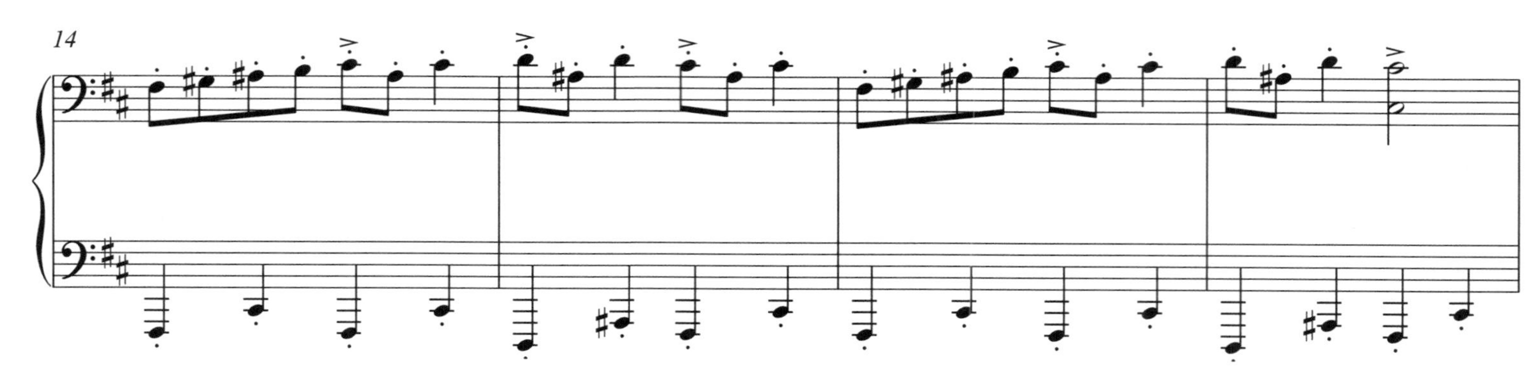

18
22
26
p
Ped.
30
poco a poco cresc. e stretto
34

38
Ped. Ped. Ped. Ped. Ped. Ped. Ped. Ped.

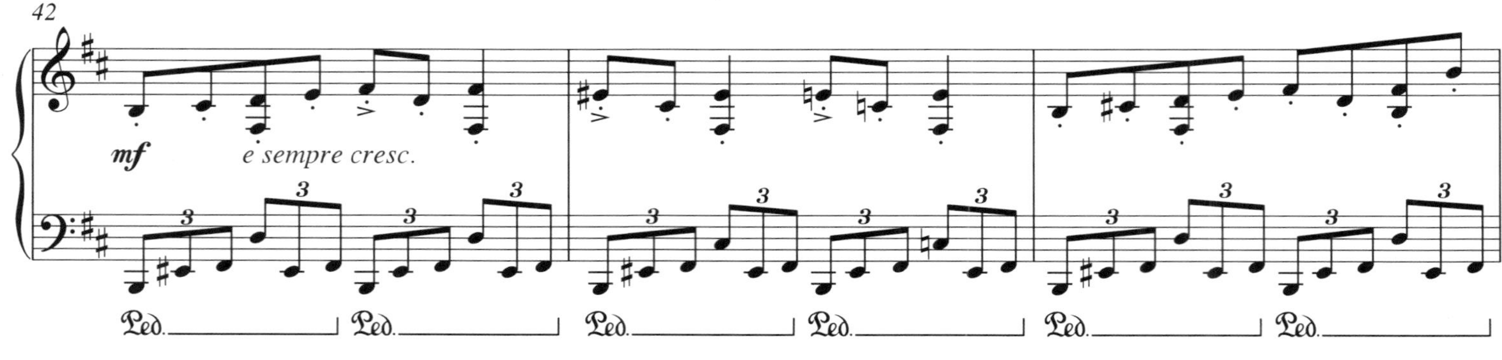
42
mf
e sempre cresc.
Ped. Ped. Ped. Ped. Ped. Ped.

45
Ped. Ped. Ped. Ped. Ped. Ped.

Più vivo
48
8va
ff
Ped. Ped. Ped. Ped.

(8)
52
Ped. Ped. Ped. Ped. Ped. Ped. Ped.

sempre stretto al fine
(8)
56
60
64
68
71
Ped.

(8)
74
loco
sfz
sfz
Ped.
Ped.
Ped.
Ped.
Ped.
Ped.
8va
78
sfz
sfz
Ped.
Ped.
Ped.
Ped.
Ped.
Ped.
(8)
82
sfz
sfz
pp
Ped.
Ped.
Ped.
(8)
85
8va
cresc. molto
p
ff
Ped.

ZURICH

633 SQUADRON

By Ron Goodwin

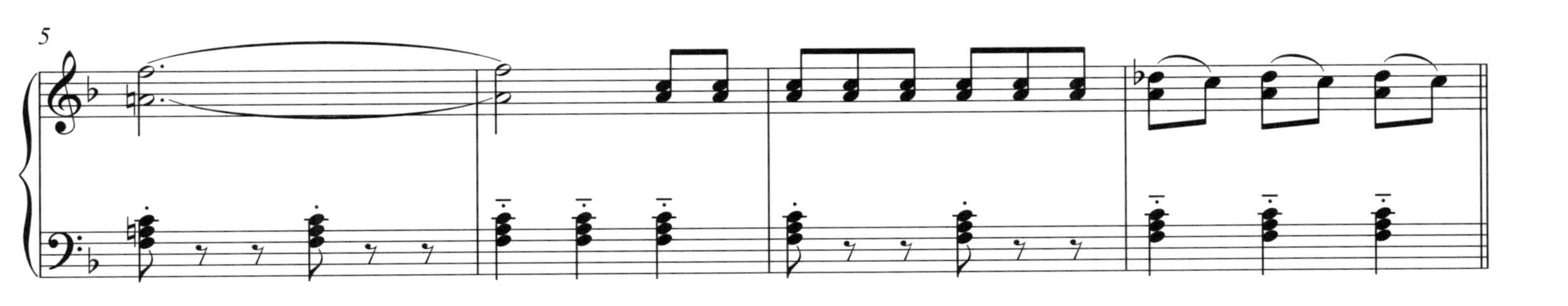

19

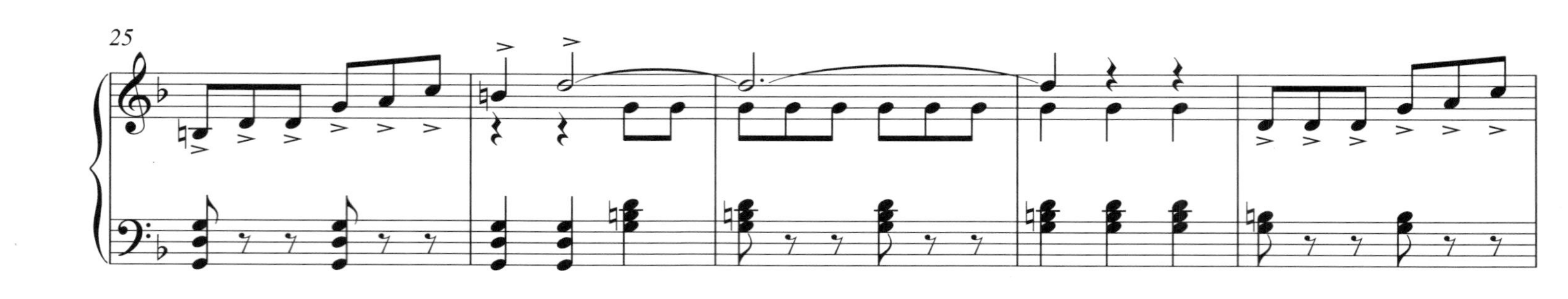
25

30

35

39
più legato

44
49
53
59
come primo
sim.
64

69

75
ff
Ped.

81
Ped.
Ped.

NESSUN DORMA

from 'Turandot'

By Giocomo Puccini

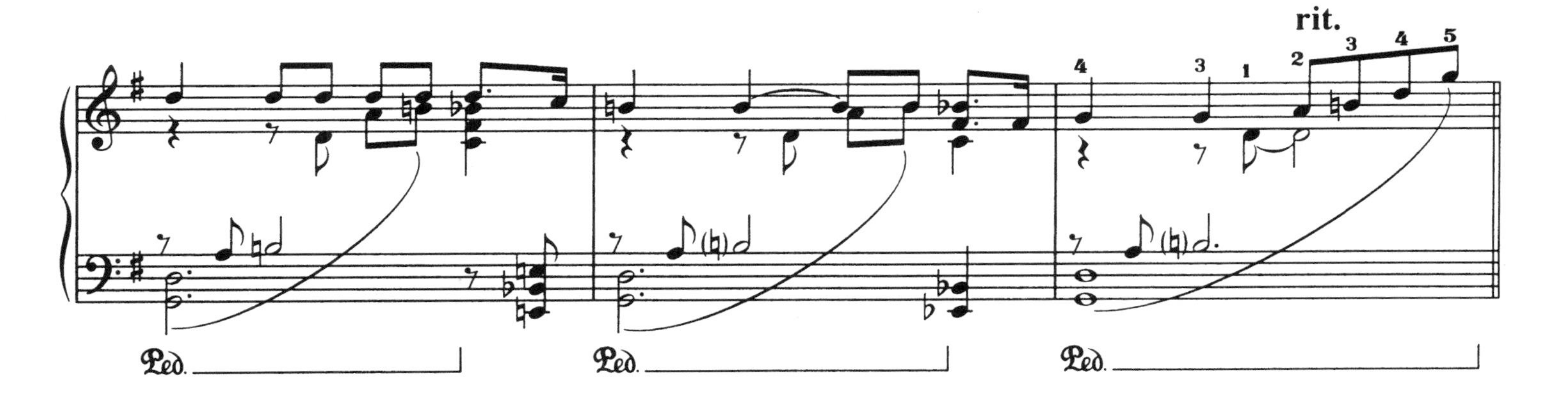

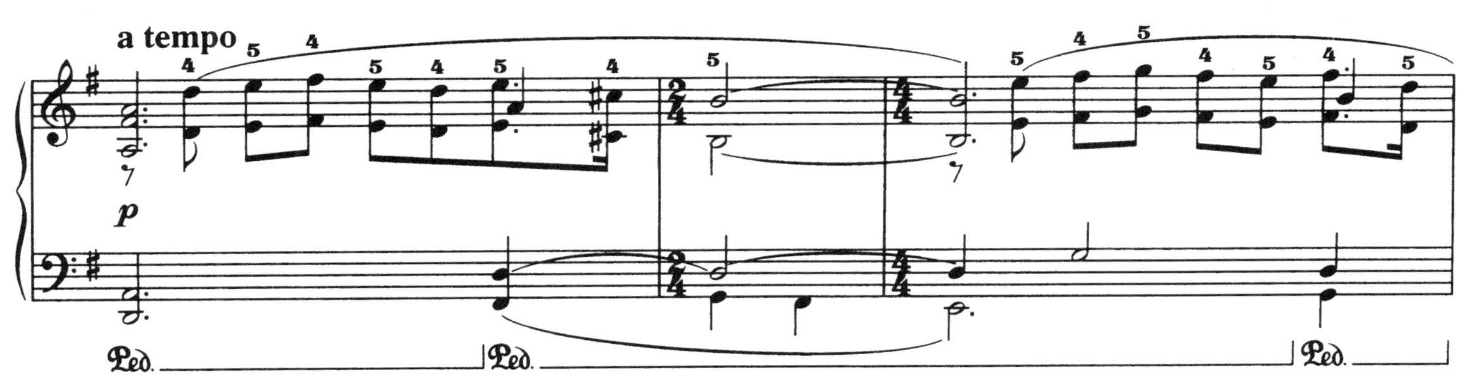

rit.

a tempo
ppp cresc.

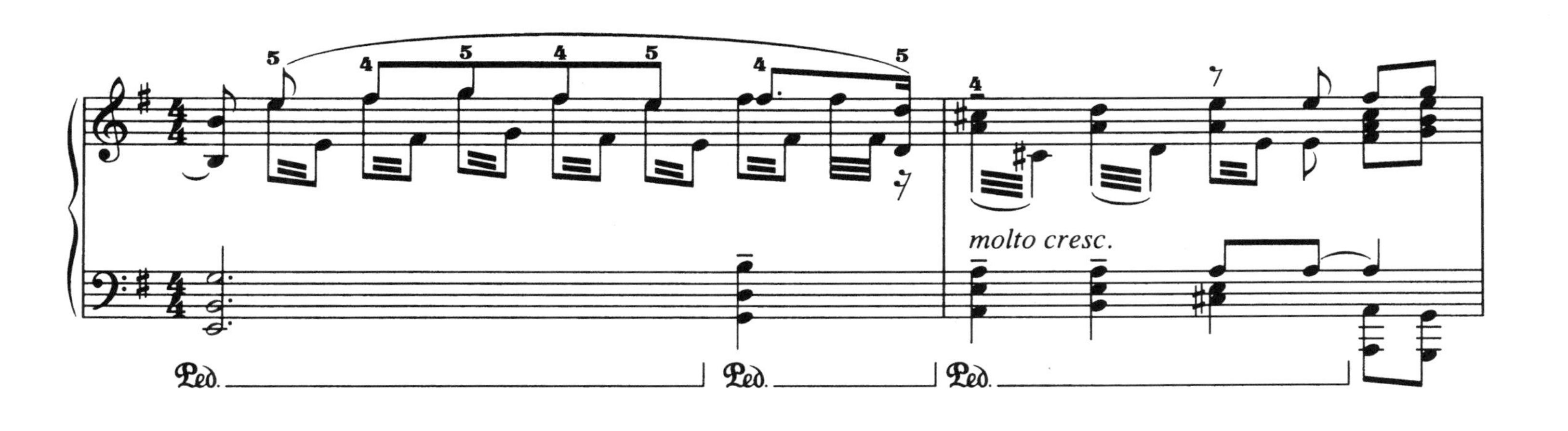
molto cresc.
Ped.
Ped.
Ped.

f
f
Ped.
Ped.
Ped.

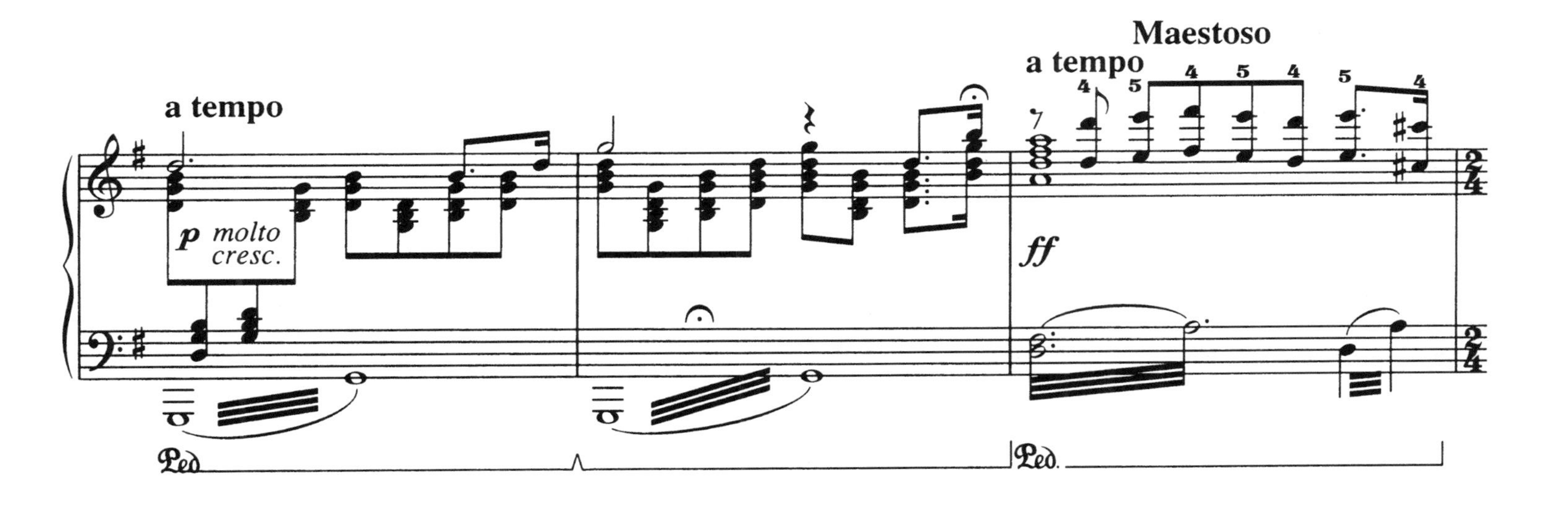
a tempo
p molto cresc.
Maestoso
a tempo
ff
Ped.
Ped.

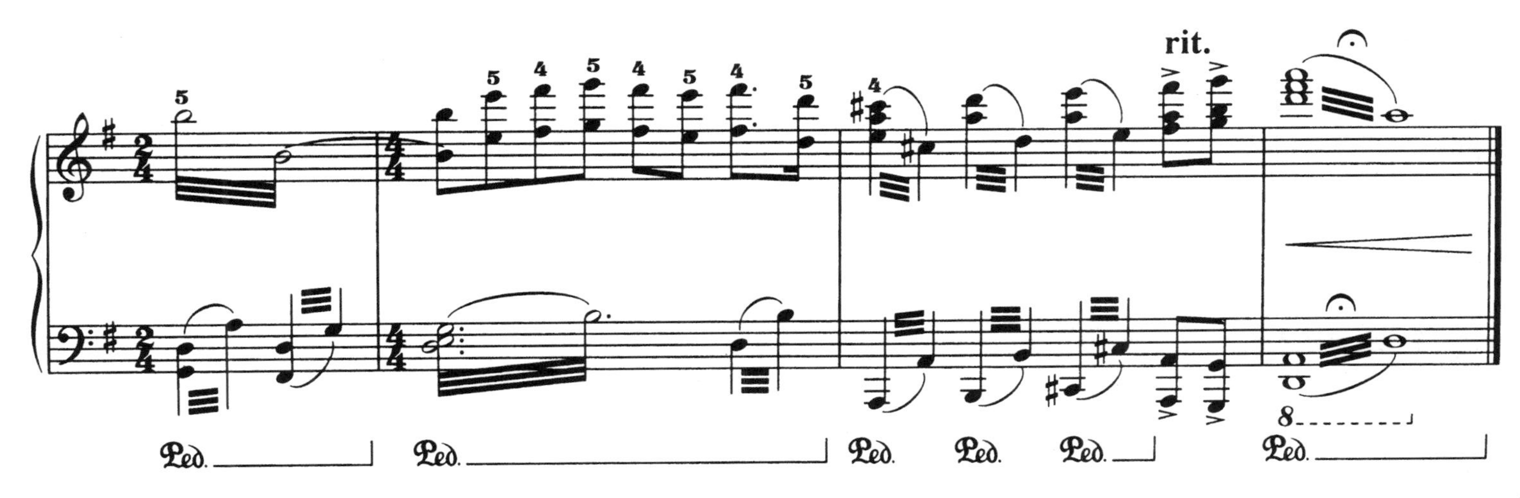
rit.
8
Ped.
Ped.
Ped.
Ped.
Ped.
Ped.

RAYMOND WEILL GENEVE WATCHES

VICTORY

By Tonci Huljic

Very rhythmic fast latin (♩ = 110)

sim.

ff

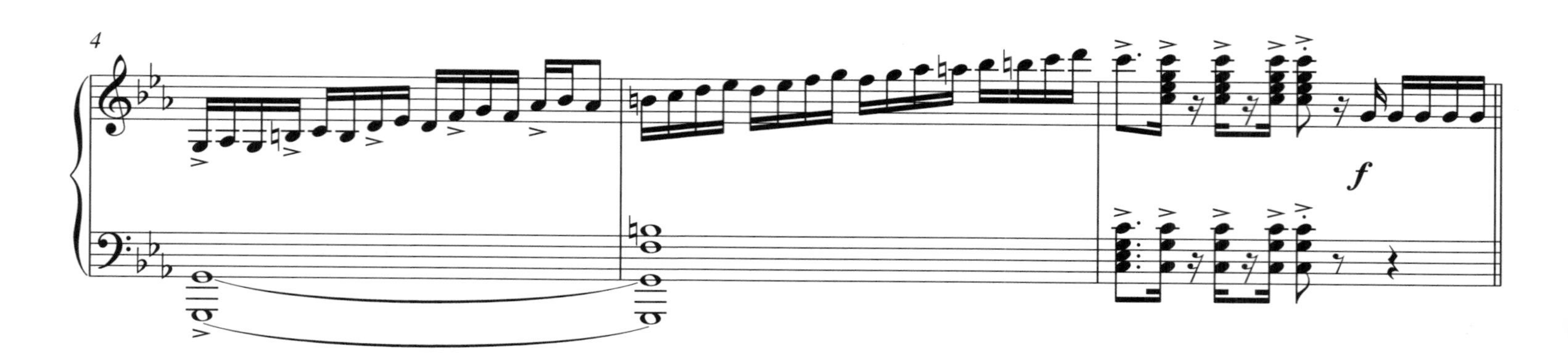

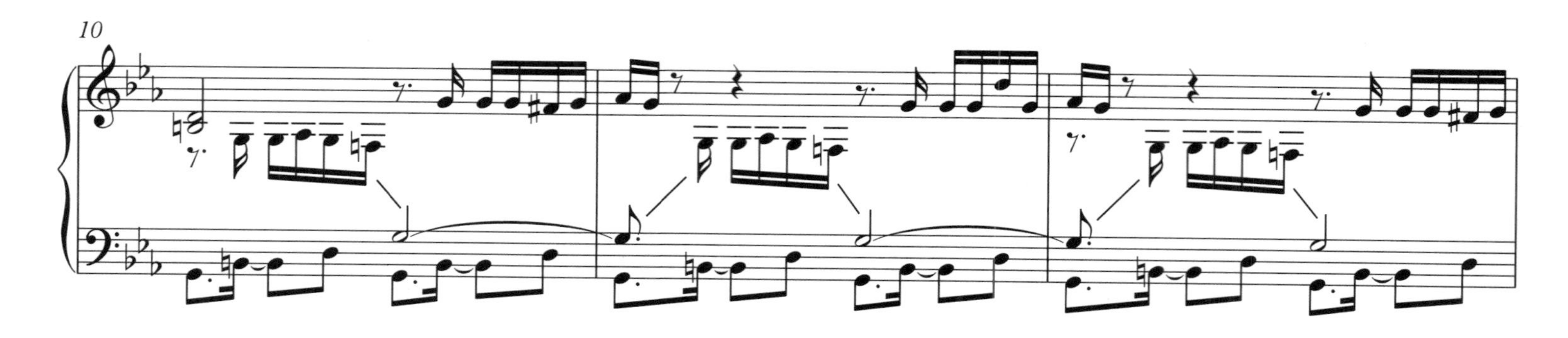

13
16
19
22
25

28
6
6
30
ff
32
34
6
6
6
7
1.
2.
36
f

MCDONALD'S RESTAURANTS LTD

THEME FROM MIDNIGHT COWBOY

By John Barry

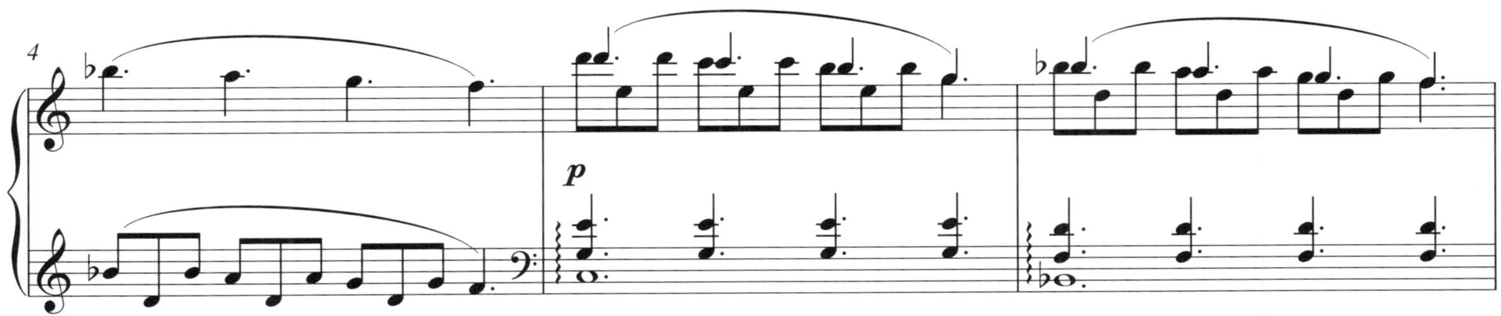

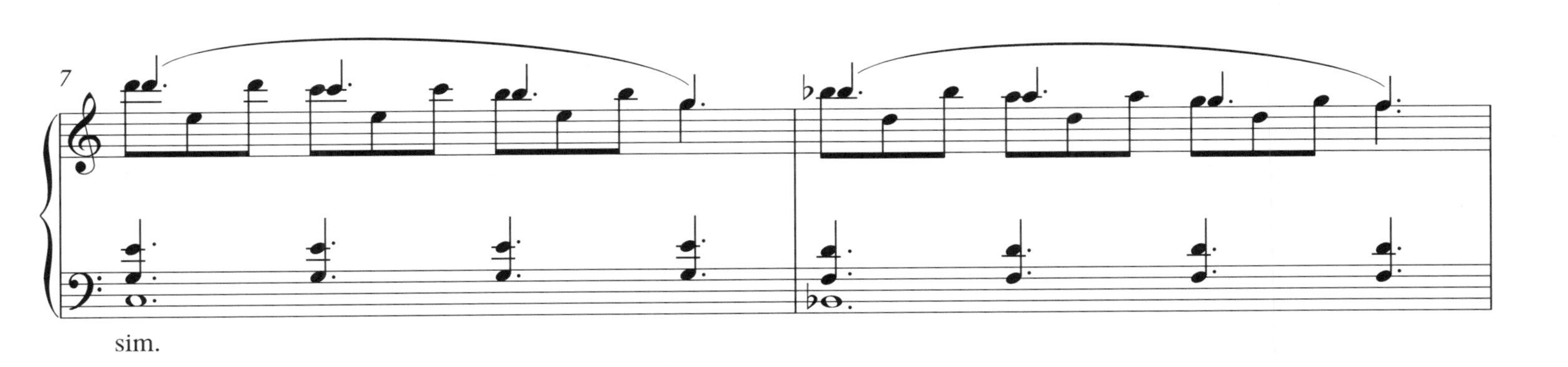

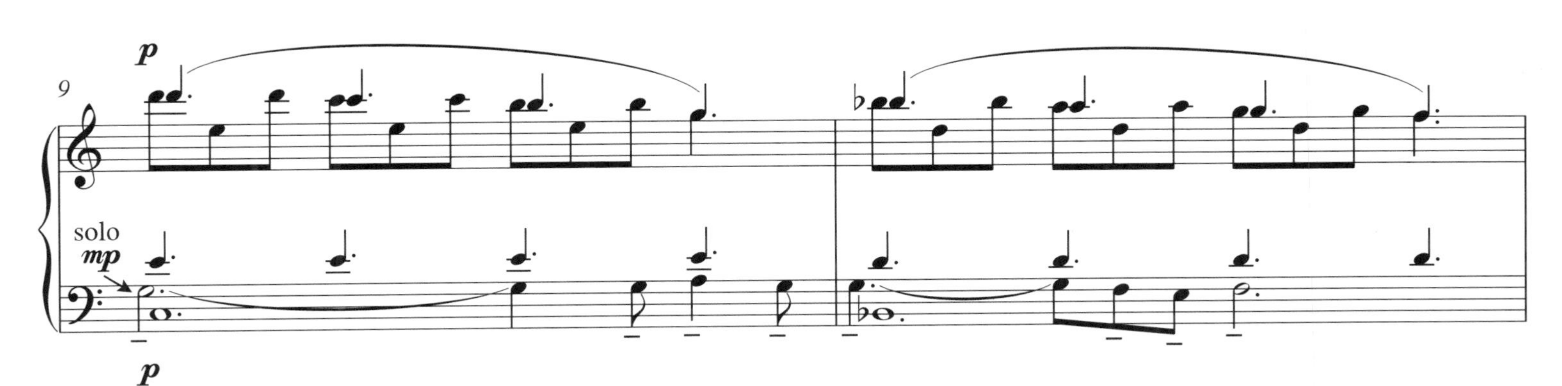

11
13
16
19
21

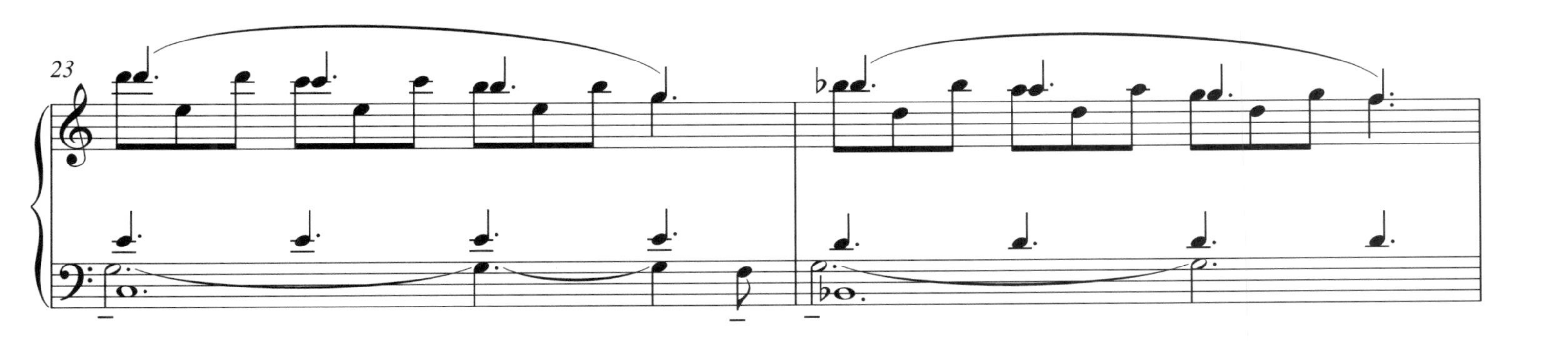
23

come prima
25
p
pp

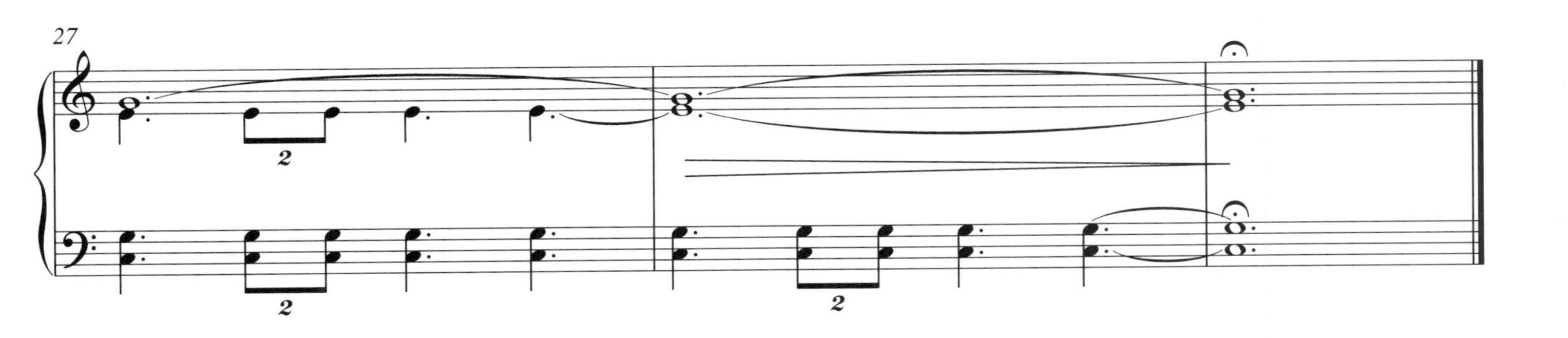
27

WALKERS CRISPS

CHASING SHEEP IS BEST LEFT TO SHEPHERDS

By Michael Nyman

16
20
LH
LH
LH
24
LH
LH
LH
LH
28
LH
Meno mosso
p
32

Più mosso ♩ = c.116
sub. mf
accel.
più mosso ♩ = c.138–154

56
60
64
68
72

76
80
84
88
92

96
Subito Tempo I
con 8va ad lib.
100
(sim.)
104
108
112

CANCER RESEARCH

FIELDS OF GOLD

By Sting

Moderato, hazily (♩ = 80 – 100)

17
21
1.
2.
ppp
25
p
29
1st time only
8va
mp
34
(8)

38
(8)
1.
loco

42
2.
3
p

46

HÄAGEN-DAZS

MAKE YOURSELF COMFORTABLE

By Bob Merrill

13
17
20
mf
23
sub. p
mf
26

29
mp
32
35
mf
38
42

45
mp
49

52
pp

RENAULT CLIO

JOHNNY AND MARY

By Robert Palmer

19
23
27
32
37
p

BLUE CROSS

NOCTURNE

By Rolf Løvland

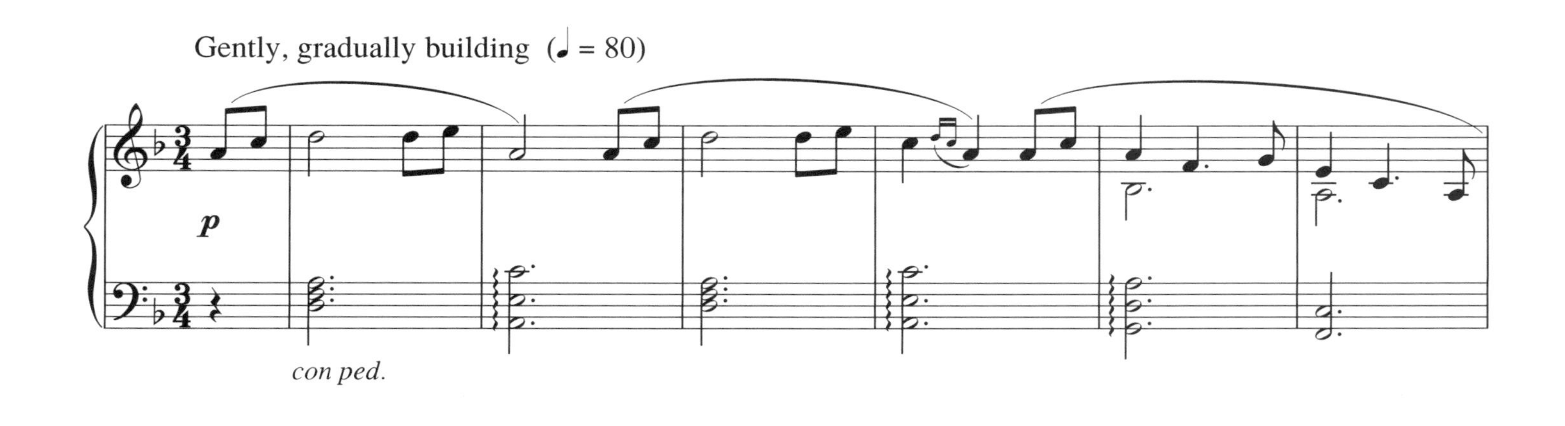

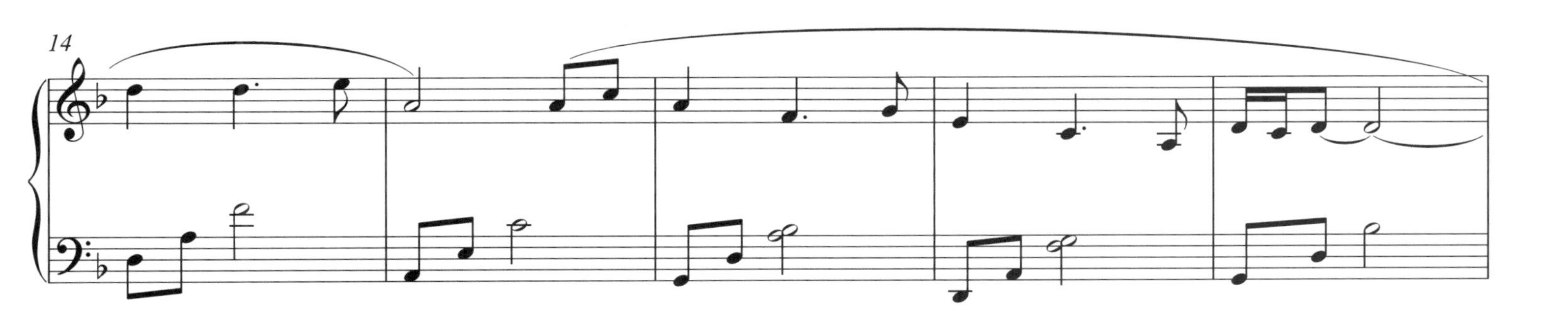

25
30
mf
35
dim.
40
mp
46

52
cresc.
58
f
63
molto dim.
68
Distantly
pp
74
rit.

STELLA ARTOIS

THEME FROM JEAN DE FLORETTE

By Jean-Claude Petit

Dm7 G7 C G7
Am G7 C Em B7
Em Dm E Am F
Dm E Am
Dm Bm7(♭5) E7 Am

FORD MONDEO

CASTA DIVA

from 'Norma'

By Vincenzo Bellini

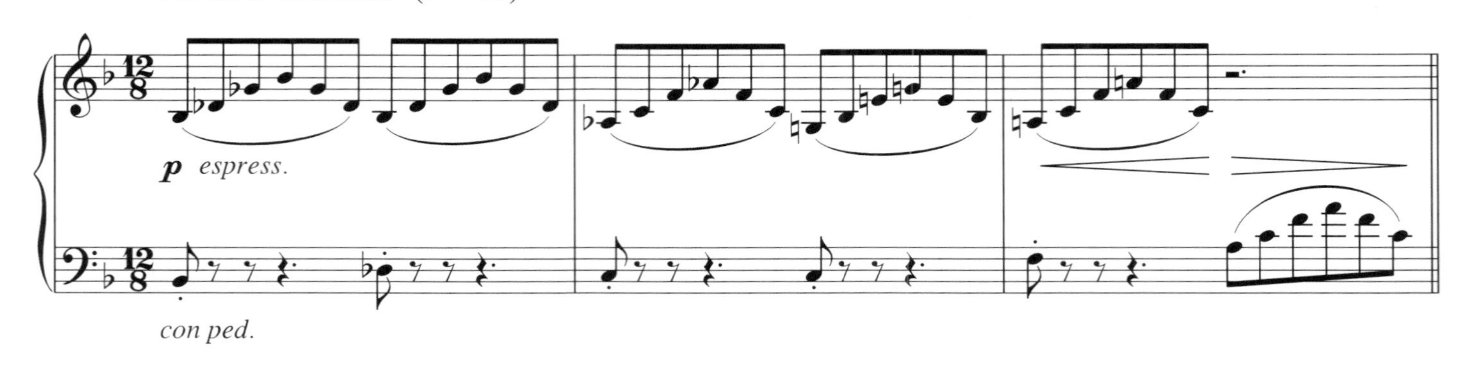

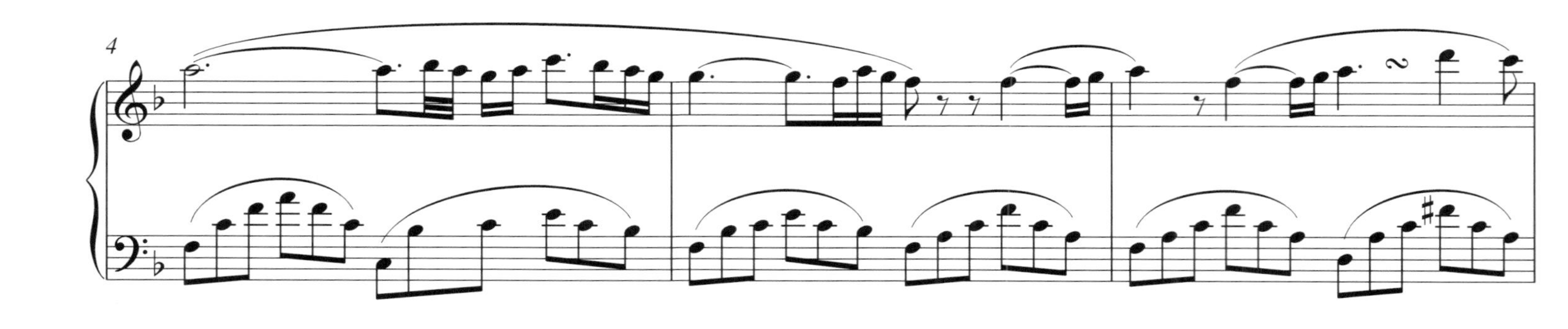

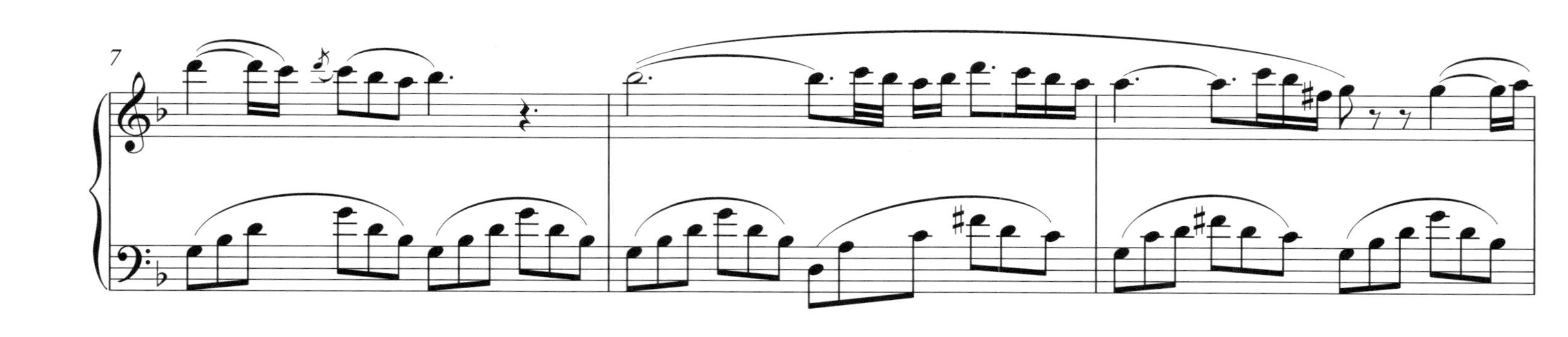

(8)
13
cresc.
f cresc.
(8)
16
ff
dim.
(8)
18
loco
pp dolce
21
24

27
pp
30
33
36
cresc.
39
f cresc.
ff

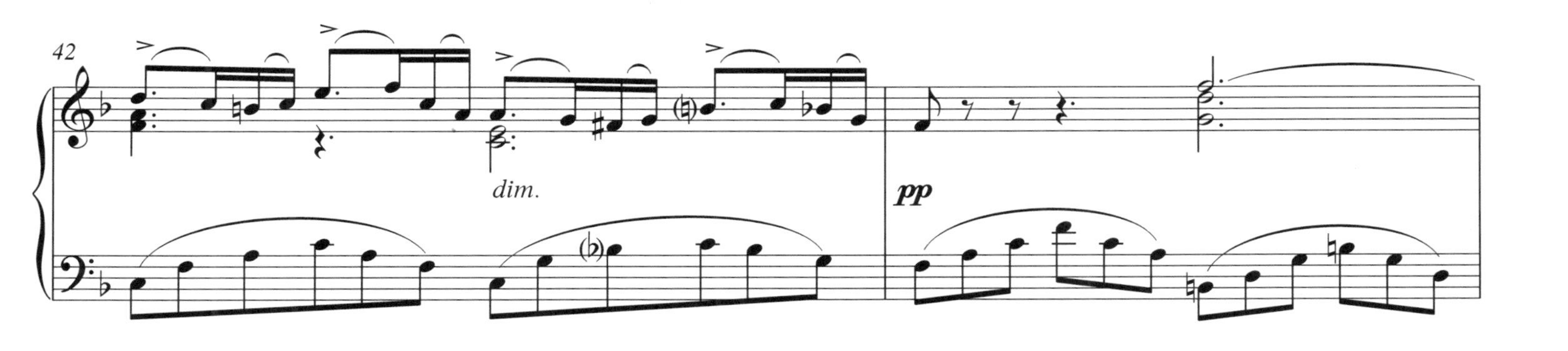
42
dim.
pp

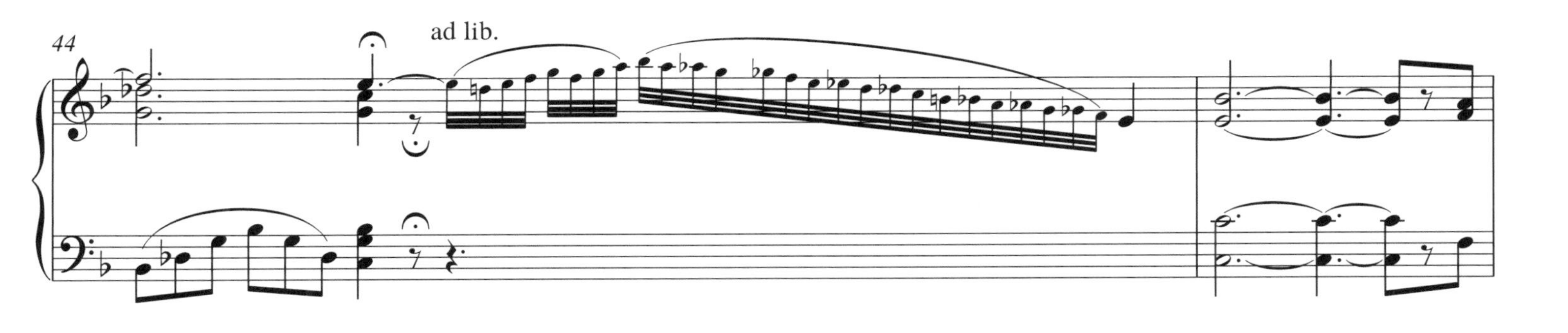
44
ad lib.

47

HELLMANN'S MAYONNAISE

WALTZ OF THE FLOWERS

from 'The Nutcracker'

By Pyotr Ilyich Tchaikovsky

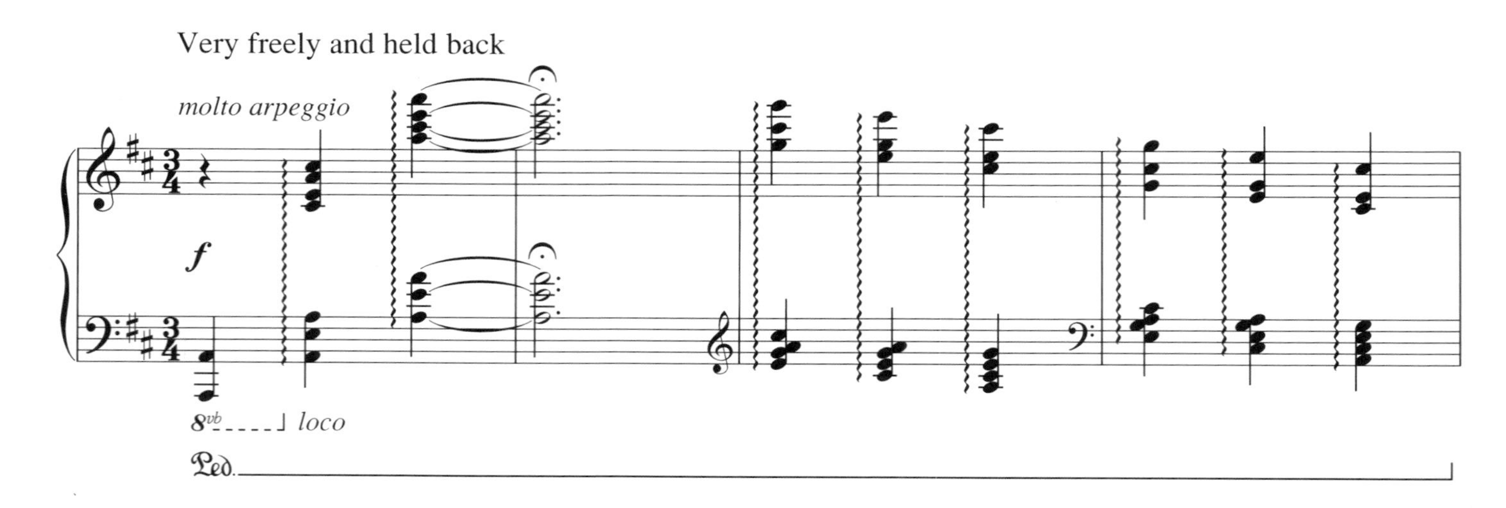

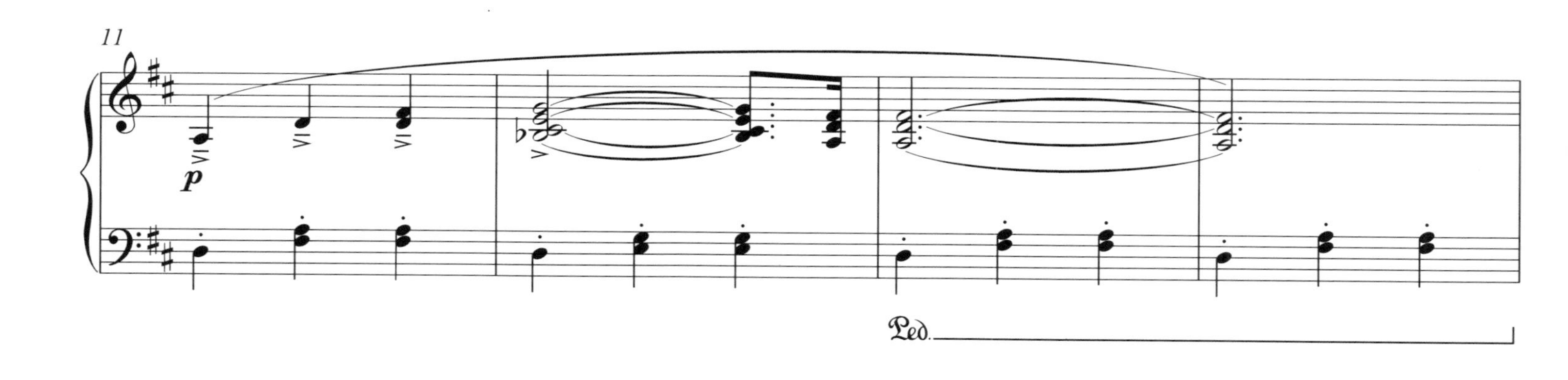

20
cresc.
24
mf
p
27
p
Ped.
31
36
cresc.
mf cresc.

40
f
43
f
3
47
3
51
3
55
cresc.
sfz

59
f
63
67
71
f cresc.
sfz
ff

HOVIS

LARGO

from 'Symphony No.9 'From The New World''

By Anton Dvorák

17
f
pp
21
25
ff
r.h.
sfz
8vb
pp
29
cresc.
33
dim.
p

37
f
pp

41